Cells, Tissues & Organ Systems: Glossary

Minerals: ....

Muscle Tissue: ....

Muscular: ....

Nerve Tissue: ....

Neuron: ....

Nutrients: ....

Oesophagus (ee-sof-a-gus): ....

Organ: ....

Plasma: ....

Receptors: ....

Red Blood Cells: ....

Sperm Cells: ....

Spinal Cord: ....

Stomach: ....

Tissue: ....

Transport: ....

Villi: ....

Vitamins: ....

1   Cells, Tissues and Organs

- Our bodies are made up of billions of ....

- Different types of cells carry out different ....

- .... cells carry .... all around the body.

- .... cells have a .... for swimming.

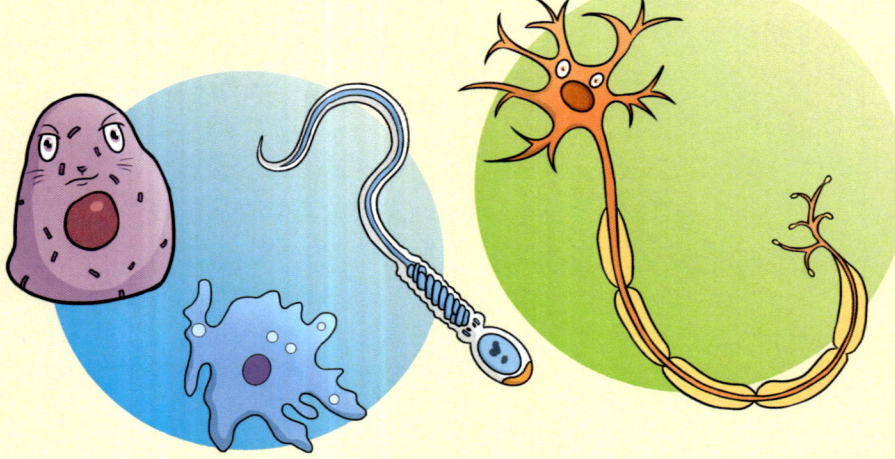
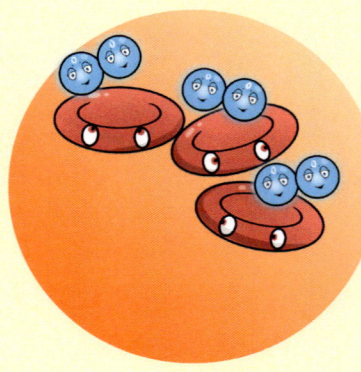

2   Tissues

- When a group of the same type of cell work together, we call it a ....

- Our .... are made up of over .... different types of tissue.

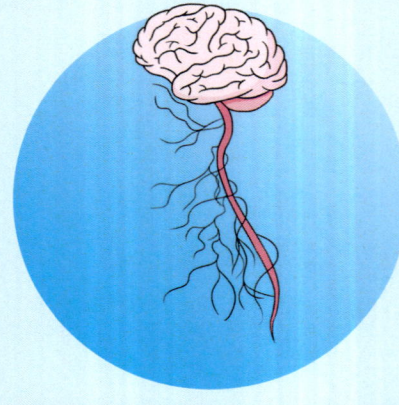

3   Tissues

- .... tissue carries messages to and from the ....

- Fatty tissue (under our skin) helps to .... our bodies.

Fatty Tissue

4 Animal Organs

- .... are made up from .... types of tissue.

- Each organ has a special ....

- Our .... is the .... organ of the body.

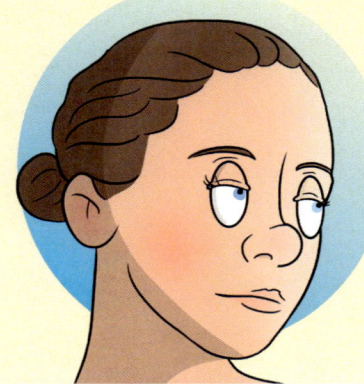

5 Plant Organs

- Plants also have ...., tissues and ....

- There is more about this in our Plant Reproduction Topic Pack.

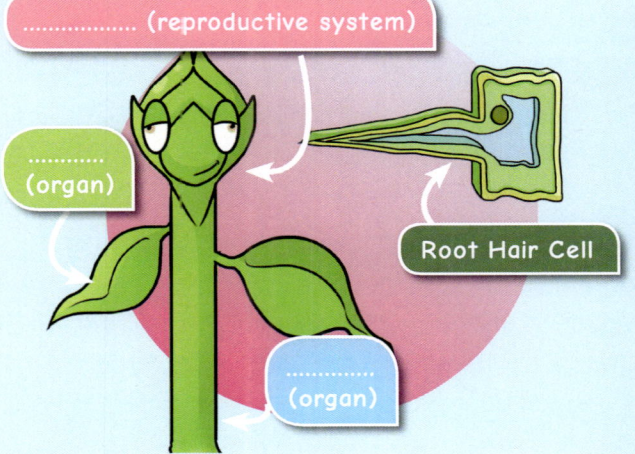

.... (reproductive system)

.... (organ)

Root Hair Cell

.... (organ)

6 Organ Systems

- Different organs ....

- Organs working together are called ....

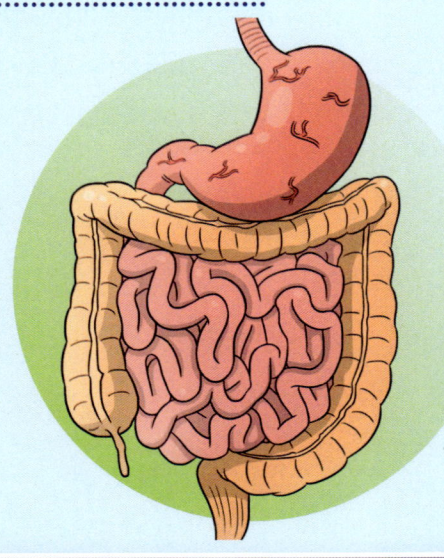

7 Working Together

- In animals the mouth, ... and .... work together.

- They are the .... system.

8   The Digestive System

- The organs of the .... system .... and .... the food we ....

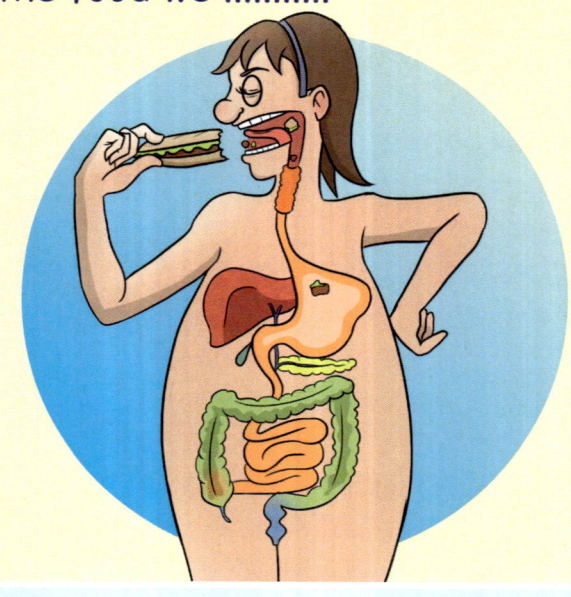

9   Different Jobs

- The different .... carry out different jobs.

10   Chewing Food

- The .... starts the .... of food by .... it.

11   Tongue

- The .... has lots of .... tissue.

- It moves the food to your .... to be ....

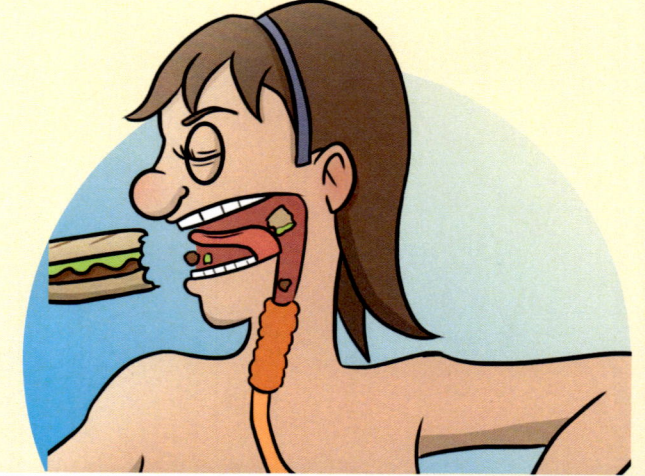

12   Stomach

- Food passes down a tube called the .... (uh-sof-ay-gus) into your stomach.

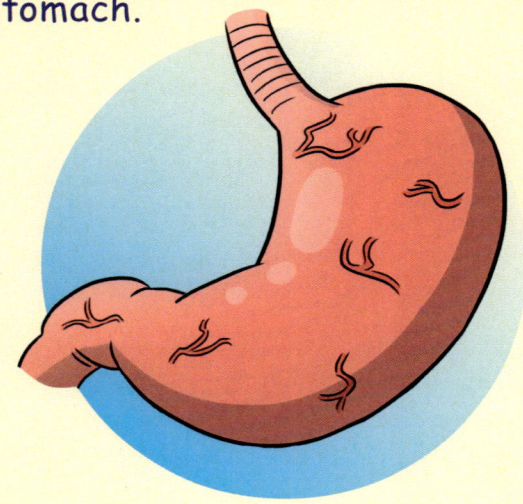

13   Muscle Tissue

- Your .... is about the size of your fist.

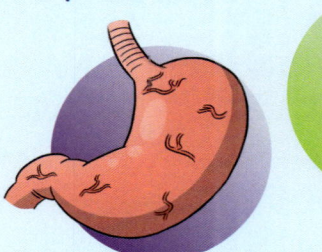

- The **stomach** looks like a small bag or a whoopee cushion!

- It has lots of .... tissue.

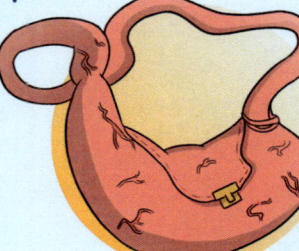

14   Contracting Muscles

- The muscle tissue gently .... and ....

- It .... the food and ....

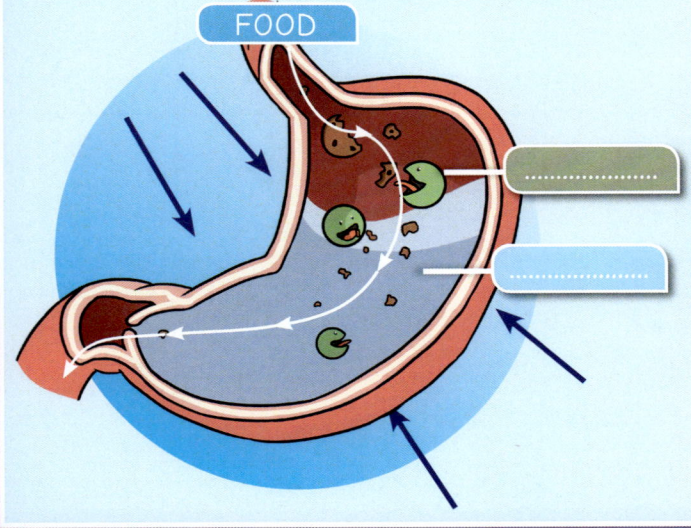

15   Small Intestine

- .... from the stomach is squeezed into the ....

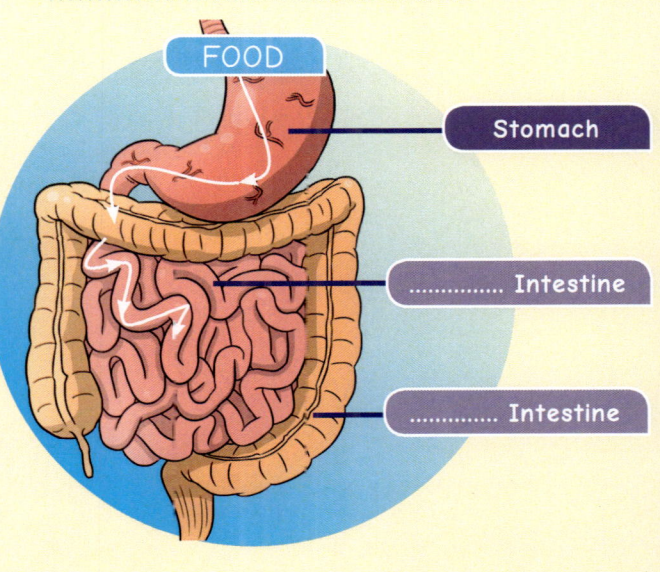

FOOD

Stomach

.... Intestine

.... Intestine

Words to help you...

undigested   villi   diameter   waves   intestine   absorb
pushes   small intestine   contract   surface   large
large   microvilli   rings   food   squeezed

16 Small Intestine

- The .... is very long (about 7m in an adult).

- It only has a small ....

- It has .... of muscle that .... in ....

- This .... the .... along.

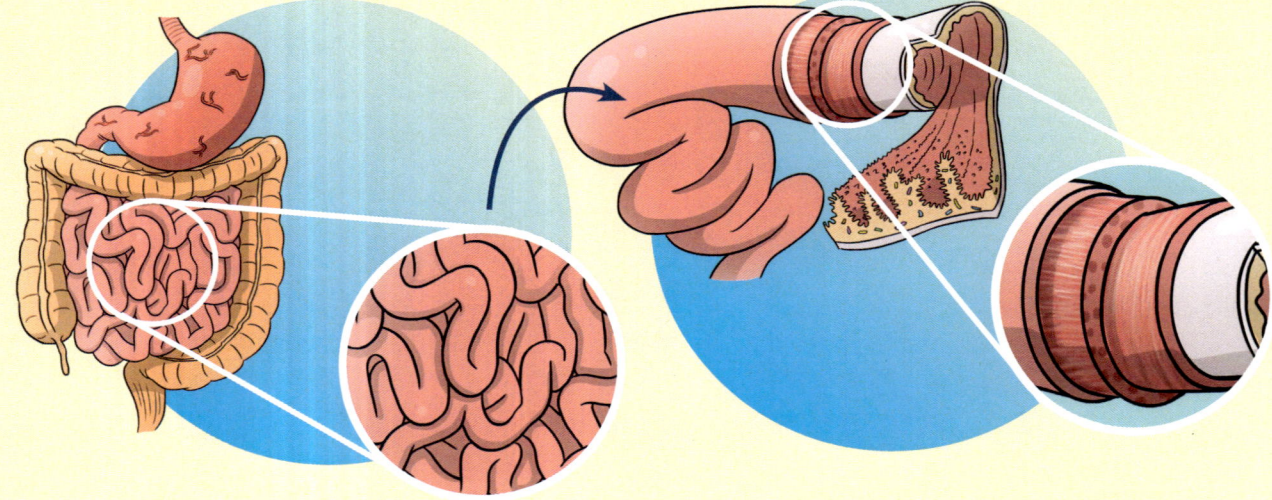

17 Increased Surface Area - An Adaptation

- The .... has lots of folds with .... and ....

- This gives it a .... surface area to .... digested food.

- The .... food is .... into the .... intestine.

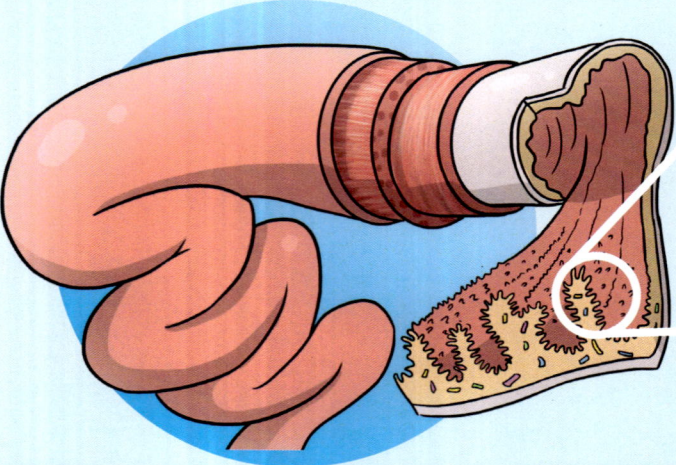
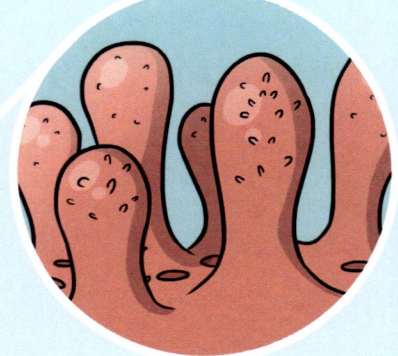

18   Large Intestine

- The large .... is quite short (about 1½m in an adult).

- It has a .... diameter.

- The large intestine has .... folds.

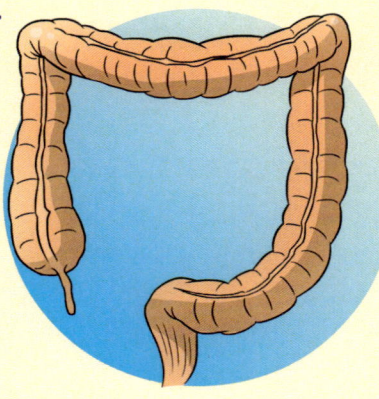

19   Absorption

- It absorbs ...., ... and ....

....

Vitamins & ....

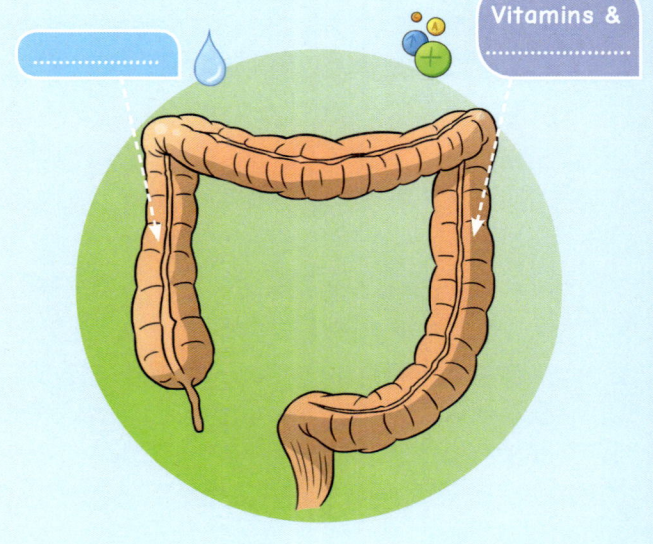

20   Bacteria

- .... breaks down the .... food before it turns into ....

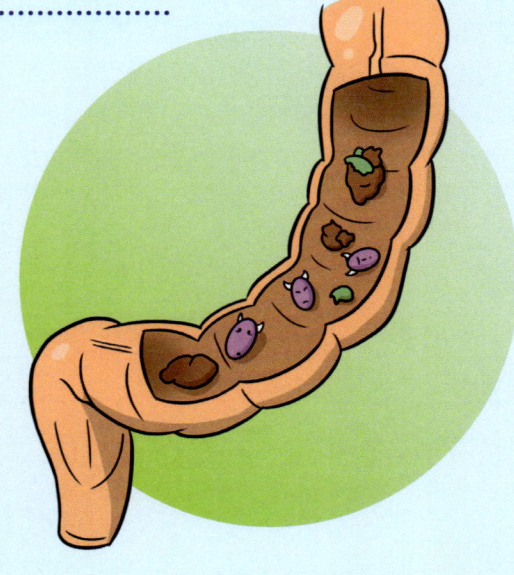

21   Undigested Food

- The .... food then leaves the body during ....

- Faeces .... the body through the ....

Words to help you...

blood   circulatory system   liquid   blood vessels   white
transport   plasma   digested   bodies   heart   cells
platelets   oxygen   red   organs   plasma

22   Transport System

- The .... is the .... system for our ....

- The blood, ... and blood vessels are .... of the circulatory system.

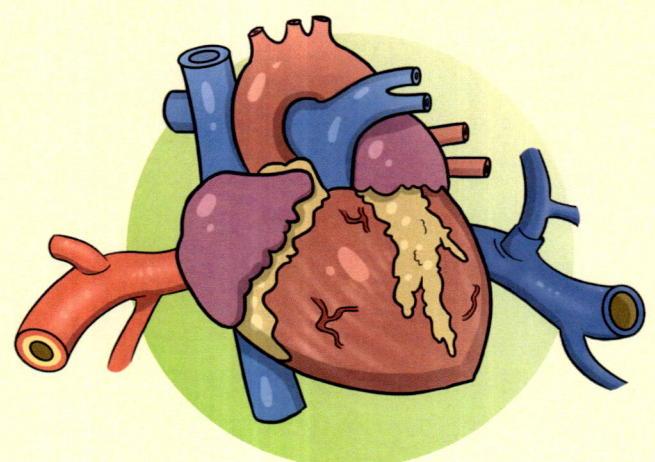
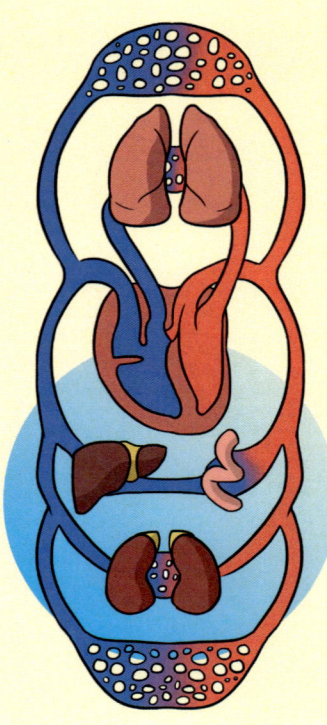

23   Transporting Nutrients and Oxygen

- It transports .... food and .... to all parts of the body.

- Our bodies have over 100,000km of ....!

- .... is made up from .... that float in a watery .... called ....

Blood Vessel

.... Blood Cells

.... Blood Cells

24 Transportation

• .... and .... products dissolve in the plasma for ....

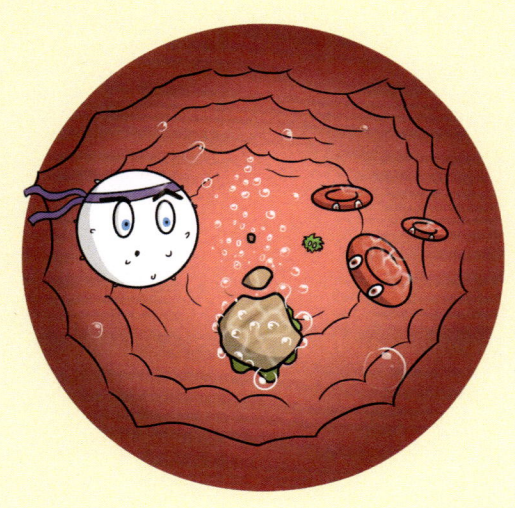

25 Important Cells

• Blood contains .... blood cells.

• They help us fight .... and ....

26 Cells With A Special Job!

• .... help the .... to .... when we have a cut.

Platelets clotting a blood vessel

Words to help you...

four   heart   right   thick muscle   oxygen   atrium
tissue   lungs   minute   organs   red blood
cardiac   left   fist   ventricle   pump

27   Red Blood Cells

• .... cells carry .... from the .... to other ....

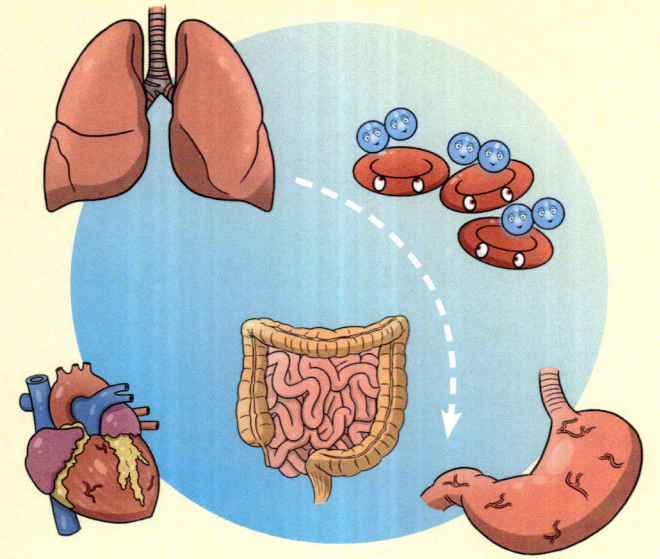

28   The Heart

• The heart, like the stomach, is about the size of a ....

• It is a .... that beats about 60 times per ....

• It will do this for 80, 90 or even 100 years.

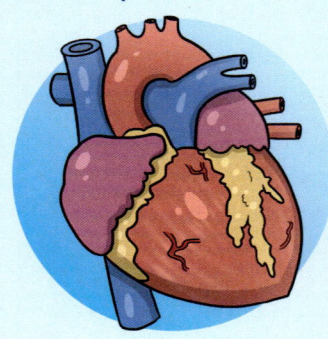

29   Cardiac Tissue

• The .... is made from a very special type of .... called .... tissue.

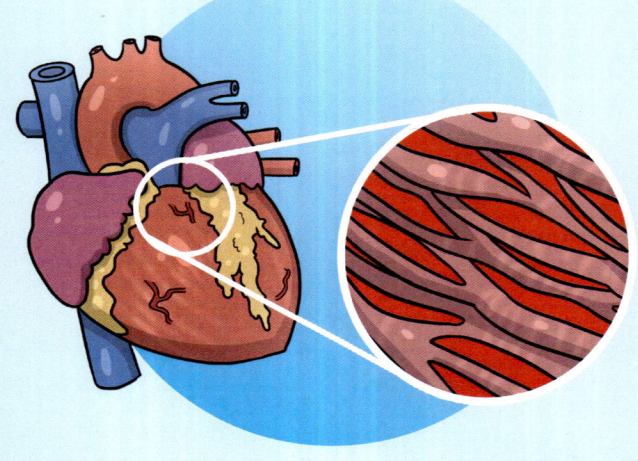

30   4 Chambers

• The heart has .... chambers surrounded by ....

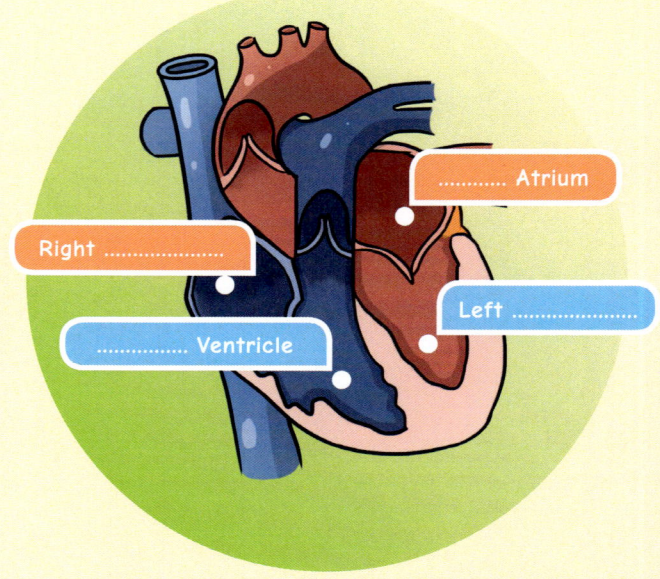

.... Atrium

Right ....

Left ....

.... Ventricle

Words to help you...

lungs   ventricle   blood   pumping
oxygen   head   collects   body   pumps   ventricle
right   blood   ventricle   bottom chambers

31   Blood from Lungs

- The left atrium collects .... from the lungs.

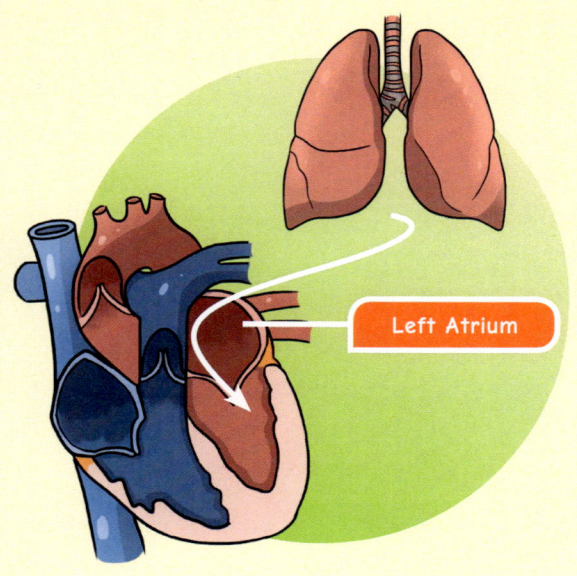

Left Atrium

32   Ventricles

- The two .... are .... chambers.

- They are the right .... and left ....

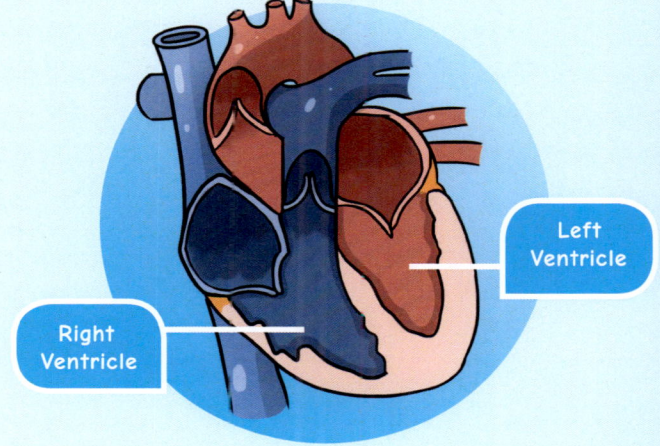

Left Ventricle

Right Ventricle

33   Blood to Lungs

- The .... ventricle .... blood from the body to the lungs.

- Blood .... oxygen in the ....

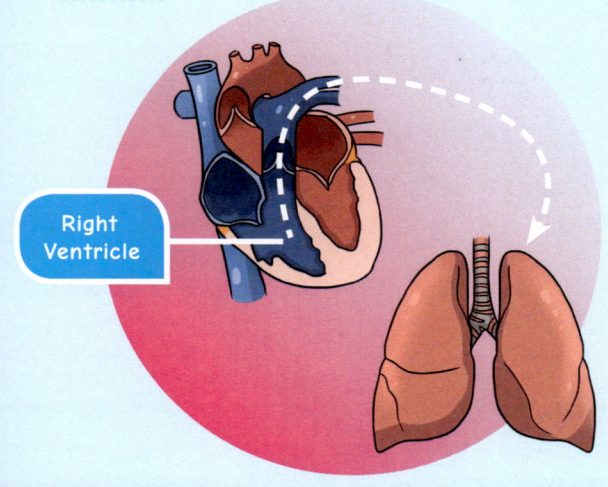

Right Ventricle

34   Oxygenated Blood
(ox-ee-jen-ay-ted)

- The left .... pumps blood full of oxygen to the .... and ....

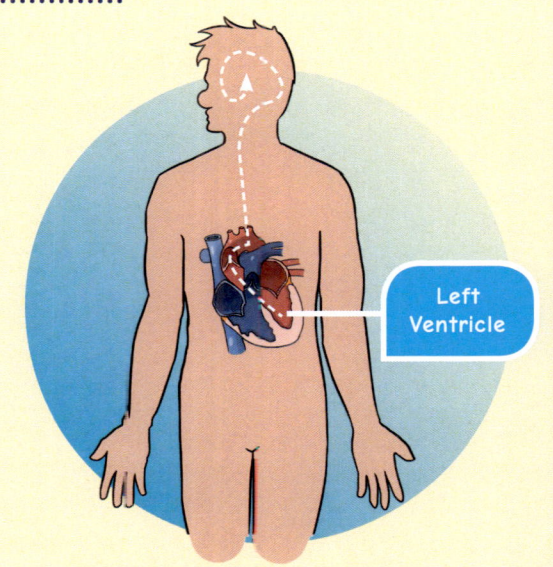

Left Ventricle

35   Heart Beat

• When the .... of the heart .... we call it a ....

• The blood is forced from the .... chambers, through the valves, into the .... chambers.

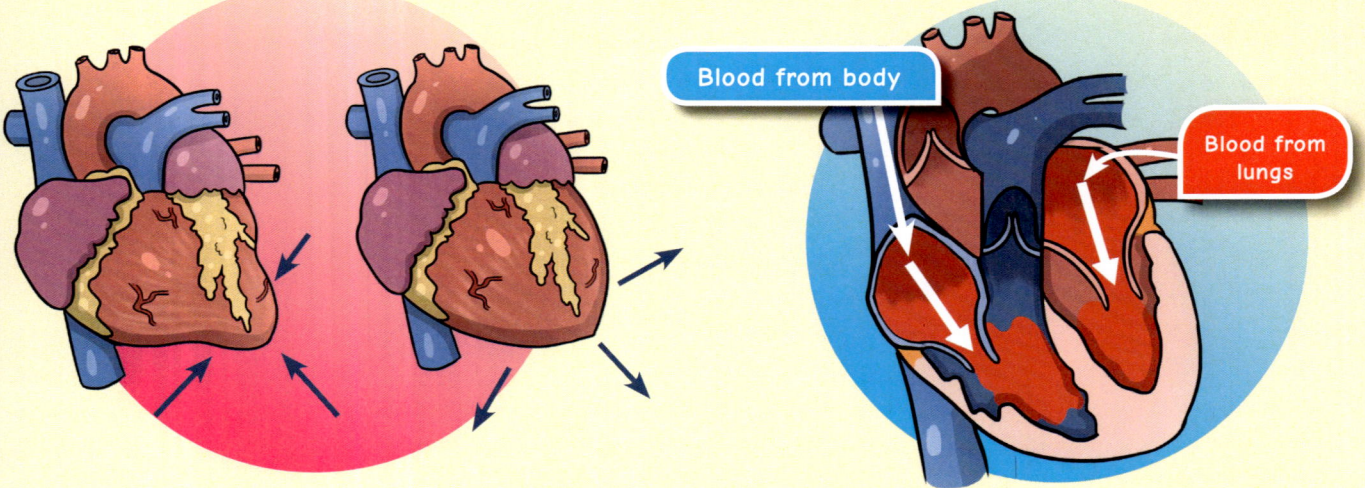

Blood from body

Blood from lungs

36   Contractions

• As heart .... continues to contract, the blood is forced out from the bottom ....

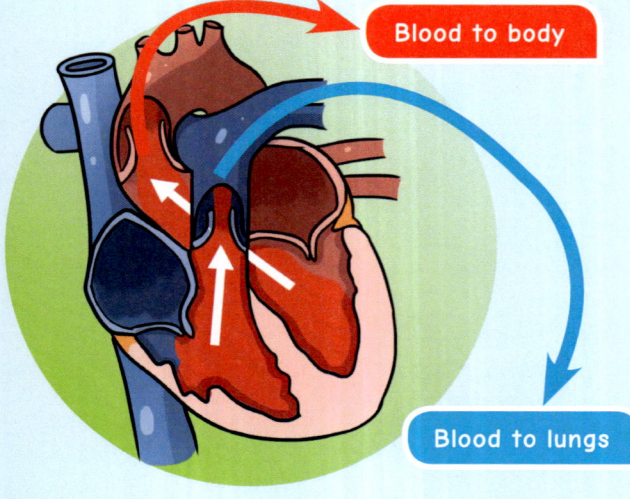

Blood to body

Blood to lungs

37   Double Circulatory (not tested for CE)

• Blood .... through the heart ...., during each .... around the body.

• It is called a .... system.

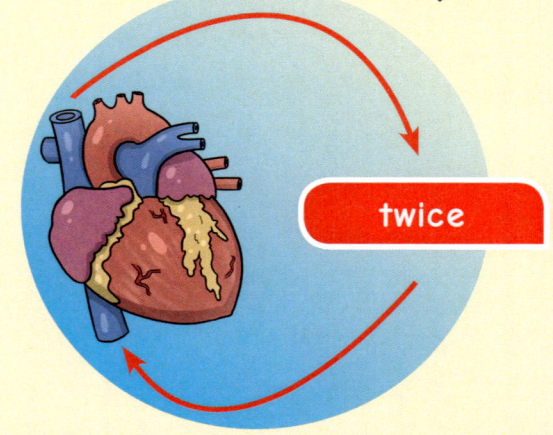

twice

Words to help you...

veins   capillary   arteries   high pressure   circulatory
blood   low   nutrients   three   elastic   vessels
tubes   delivered   thin   collected   cells   thick

38   Blood Vessels

- The .... system consists of the heart pumping .... through the blood .... of the body.

- As the blood goes around the body, it goes through .... types of blood vessels.

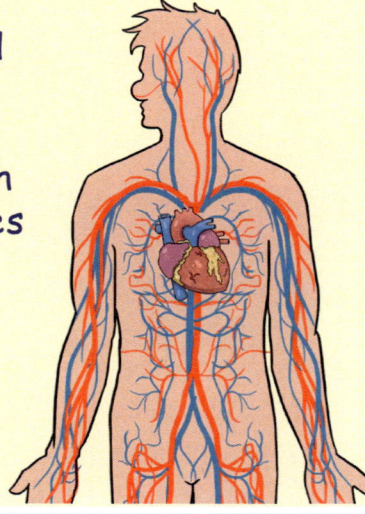

39   1. Arteries

- .... are .... that have .... walls made from muscle and .... tissue.

- Arteries carry blood at .... away from the heart. They are like motorways.

A= Away from heart

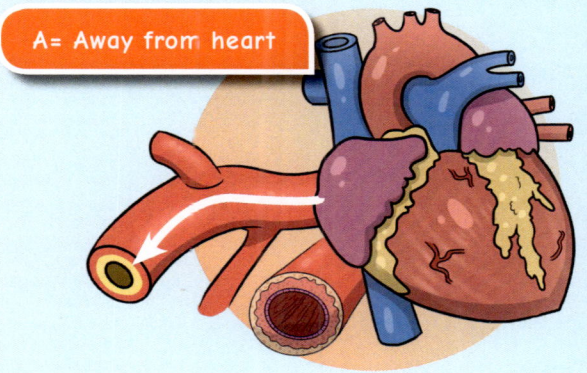

40   2. Veins

- .... are tubes with .... walls made from muscle and elastic tissue.

- Veins carry .... pressure blood towards the heart.

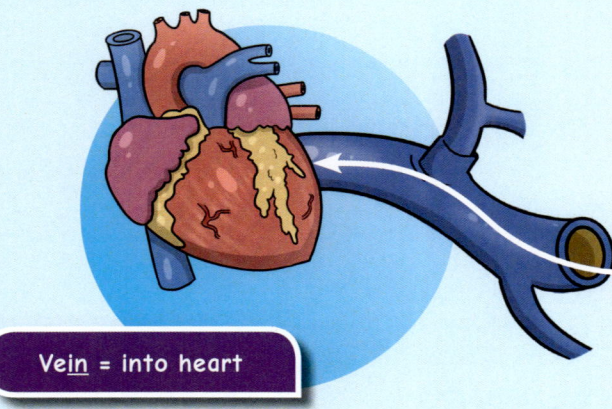

Vein = into heart

41   3. Capillaries

- .... walls are just one cell thick.

- .... are .... to .... and waste is .... through the capillaries.

- They are like narrow roads in the town where things go slowly and can drop stuff off.

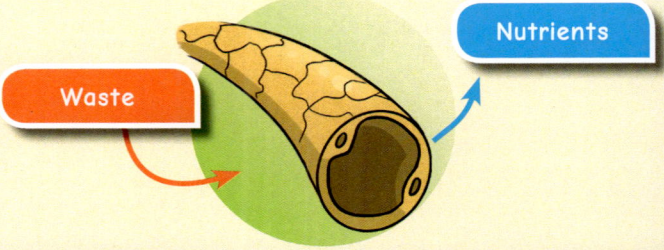

Waste

Nutrients

42 The Nervous System (not tested for CE)

- The .... system is .... into 2 parts.

- .... (Central Nervous System)

- .... Nervous System

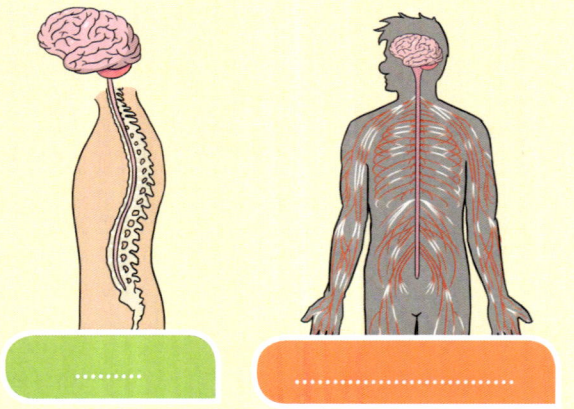

43 Central Nervous System

- The .... Nervous System (CNS) is made up of the ...., and spinal cord.

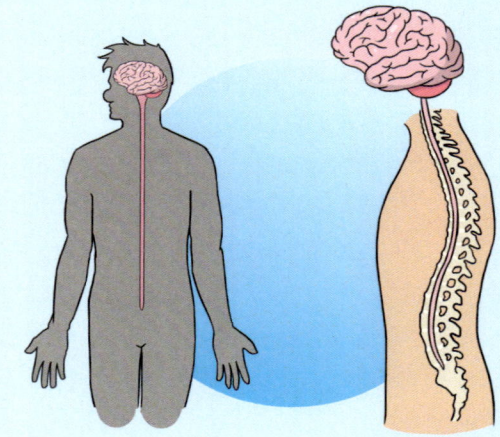

44 Nervous System

- The .... carries .... from receptors to the brain.

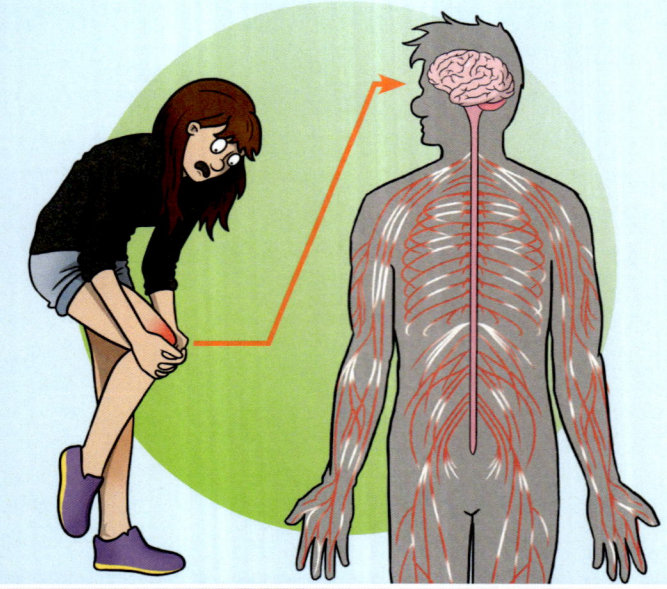

45 Peripheral (per-if-er-al) Nervous System

- The .... nervous system is made up from all other nerves (.....................) and ....

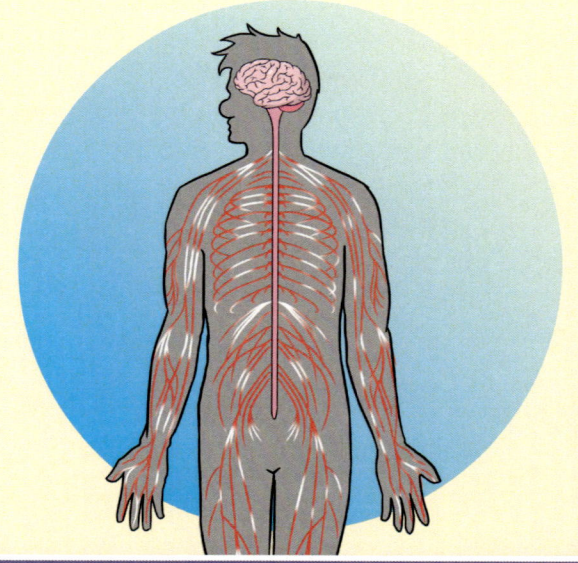

46 Spinal Cord

- The .... nervous system connects the .... through the ....

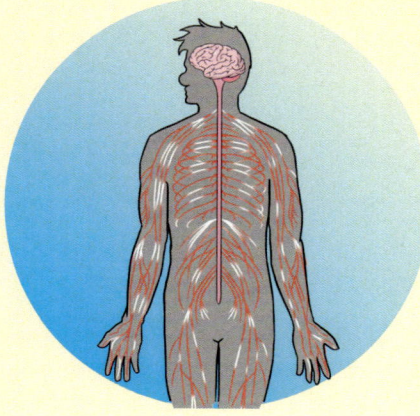

47 Neurons

- Neurons .... all parts of the nervous .... together.

- Neurons carry ....
signals.

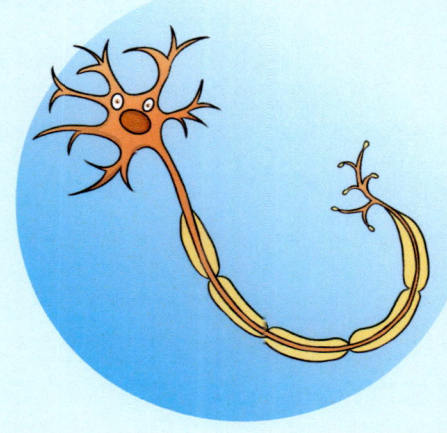

48 Longest Neuron!

- The longest .... reaches from our big toe to our ....

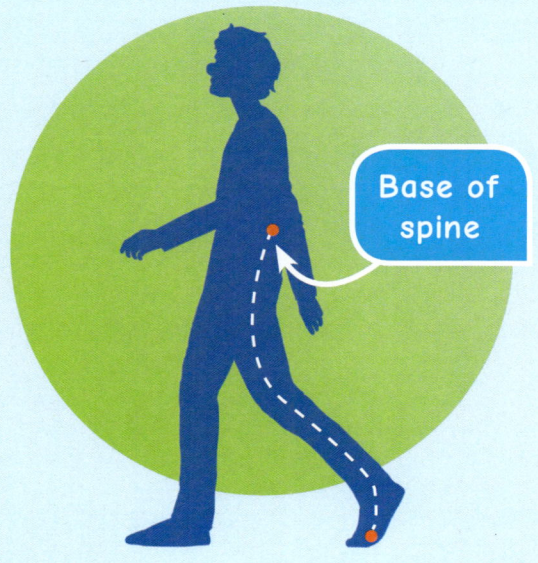

Base of spine

49 Sensory Neurons

- .... neurons carry ....
from .... to the brain.

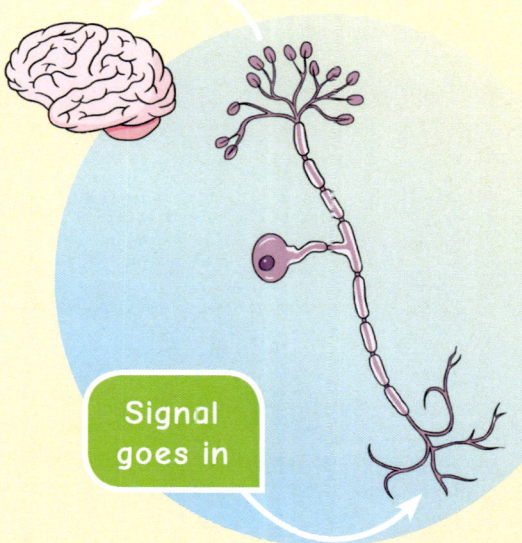

Signal goes in

Organs in a Plant

- Remember: plants are living o......................... too!
- They are made up of different cells.
- As the plant grows, the cells develop to make plant t........................... and o.........................
- The organs let the plant perform life p..............................

F.................... are **organs** needed for reproduction

- C...................... and s...................... attracts insects for pollination.
- The flower makes the s............ cells.
- When the petals fall, the flower becomes the f...........................
- The fruit contains the s...........................

The s............. is an **organ** needed for reproduction and nutrition.

- It h.................... the flower up for insects and wind pollination.
- It holds the leaves up to the light for p..
- It contains tubes that let w...................... and n........................... move around the plant (transport system).

R................ are **organs** needed for nutrition and keep the plant in place.

- They hold the plant in the s.......................
- They grow down to find w...........................
- They have root hair cells adapted to a.................... water and n........................... from the soil.

L................ are **organs** needed for nutrition.

- C........................... traps sunlight for photosynthesis.
- They have a l.................... surface area for photosynthesis.
- They have cells adapted to let gases d...................... in and out.

1 Energy is ....

- Energy is work that has been .... or work that is able to be done.

- For any work (or job) to ...., energy has to be ....

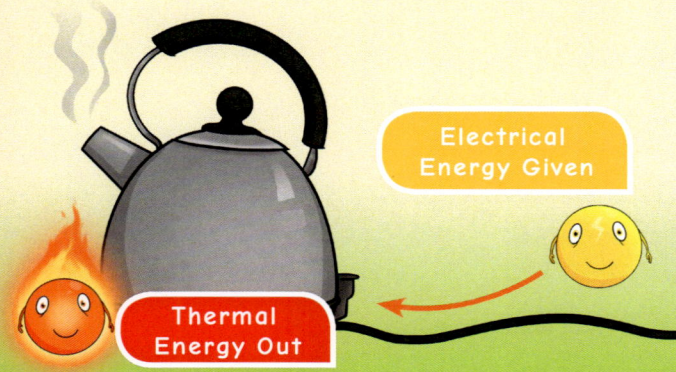

2 Job = Activity

A 'job' can be any ....:

- A person eating.

- A lorry ....

- A kettle ....

- A TV working.

3 Joules (j)

- The size of the .... is the work done.

- Work is measured in .... (j).

Work is measured in joules (j)

4 Energy = Work

The more .... supplied, the .... work can be done.

- The faster you run, the more energy you need.

- The .... you jump, the more energy you need.

- The more soil you move, the more energy you need.

Forms of Energy

.... Energy

During a chemical change, energy is released.

.... Energy

- When particles .... they give out energy in the form of sound waves.

- Sound waves travel through liquids, solids and gases.

- They do <u>not</u> travel through a vacuum.

.... Energy (KE)

- Anything .... has kinetic energy.

- The kinetic energy in a body depends upon:
The mass (m) of the moving object.
The speed (v) of the moving object.

.... Energy (or heat energy)

- Everything is made of molecules.

- These are always moving so they have kinetic energy.

KS3 ONLY:
- The total of all the KE in a substance is called the internal energy.

- The form of energy that makes the internal energy increase is called thermal energy (or heat energy).

.... Energy

- Energy from the Sun is transferred by waves.

- Light waves are a type of electromagnetic wave.

- They are energy that we can see.

.... Energy

- Electric currents move ....

- When things are moved, work has been done so we know energy has been used.

- Electrical energy is used to make things happen.

.... Energy (PE)

- This is energy that something has because of its position or condition.

- It is the work that is **able to be done.**

.... Potential Energy (GPE)

GPE depends upon:

- The .... (m) of the body.

- The vertical .... (h) it can fall through.

- The force of gravity (g) acting on it.

Example: A large skydiver has more GPE than a smaller person.

.... Potential Energy

- The more .... you put on a spring, the more energy it will gain.

- The more turns you make on a wind up toy, the faster or further it will go.

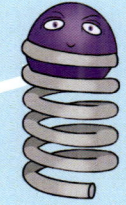

5   Energy ....

- Energy is never used up. It just .... from one form to another.

- This makes the energy ....

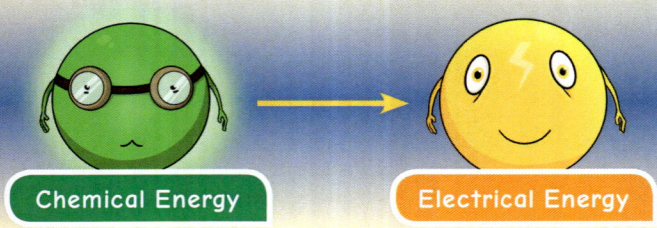

- .... of energy: Total amount of energy at the start = Total amount of energy at the end.

6   Energy Transformation

- .... in sunlight can be changed into .... energy.

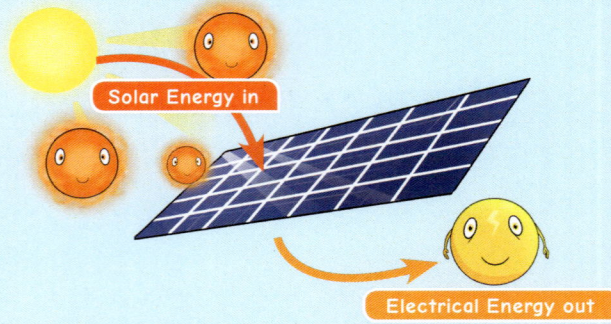

- A lamp changes electrical energy into .... and ....

BUT when we change energy from one form to another, some energy is <u>useful</u> and some is <u>wasted</u>.

7   Energy Chain

- Energy chains show how energy is ....

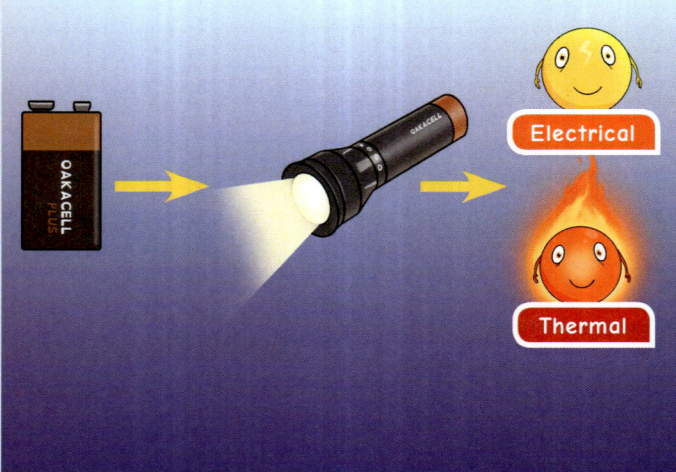

8   Thermal Energy Wasted

- .... energy (heat) is always released. This is usually .... energy.

9 .... Potential Energy

• Wind up cars use a .... to .... them.

• The spring .... elastic potential energy.

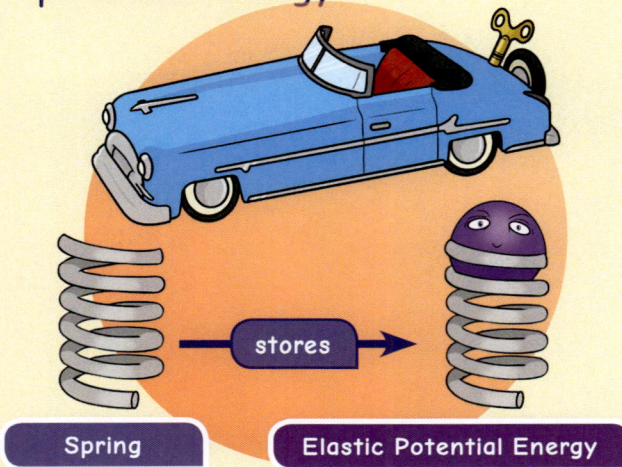

stores

Spring → Elastic Potential Energy

10 Transforming Energy

• As we .... up the car, we .... kinetic energy into elastic potential energy.

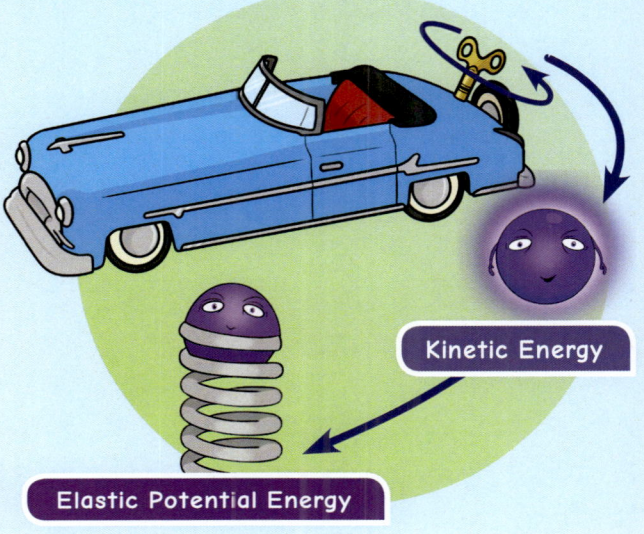

Kinetic Energy

Elastic Potential Energy

11 Transforming Energy

• The .... then uses the elastic .... energy and transforms it into .... energy.

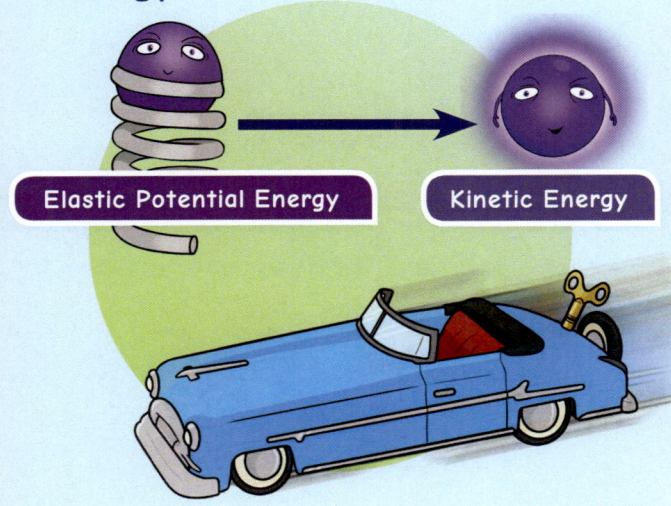

Elastic Potential Energy → Kinetic Energy

12 Electrical Energy

• .... energy is a very useful form of ....

This booklet is not to be photocopied. Thank you.

3

13   Electrical Energy

- Electrical energy can be transformed to many .... forms of energy.

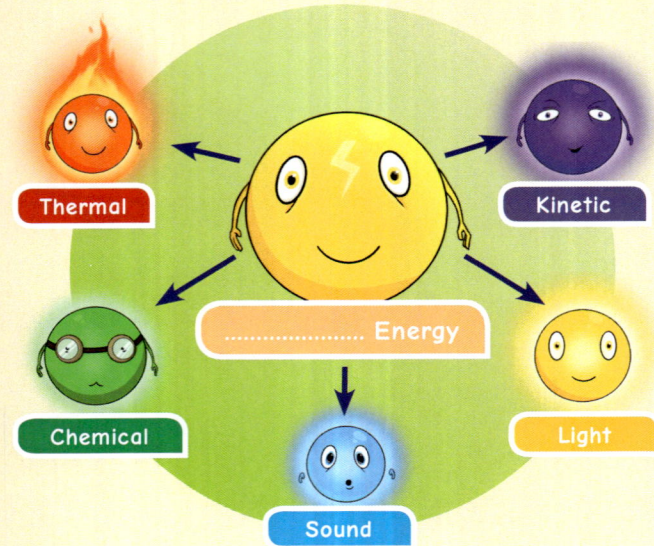

14   A Television

- A TV set .... electrical energy into .... and light energy.

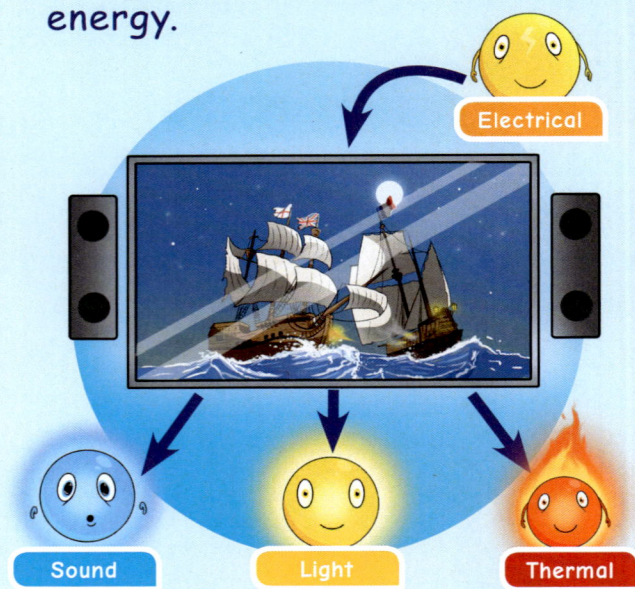

15   A Washing Machine

- A washing machine transforms electical energy into ...., sound and kinetic ....

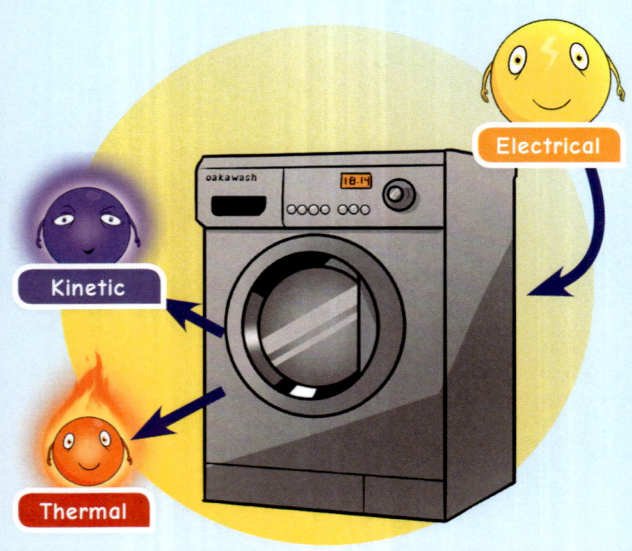

16   Storing Energy

- Energy can be ....

- The stored energy in .... is called .... energy.

- .... are an example of stored chemical energy.

17   Potential Energy

- Springs store .... energy.

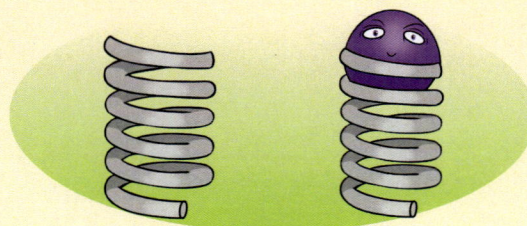

- Flywheels (in machines) store .... energy. (KS3 ONLY)

18   Wasted Energy

- When energy is transformed, from one .... to another, not all of the energy transformation is ....

- Some energy is ....

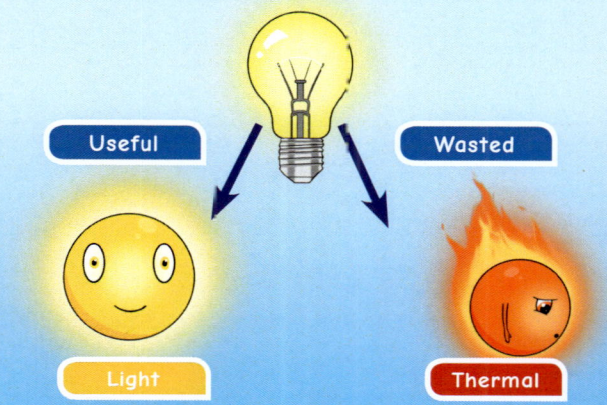

Useful   Wasted

Light   Thermal

19   Useful & Wasted Energy from ....

- We .... the chemical energy in our food into kinetic ....

- Some of the chemical energy in our food is transformed as .... energy.

- We need energy for life .... like ....

Chemical

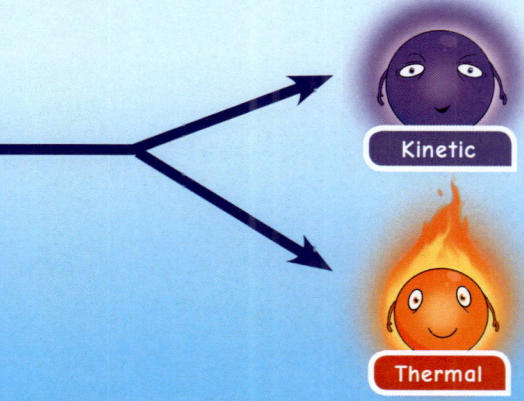

Kinetic

Thermal

This booklet is not to be photocopied. Thank you.

5

20   Food Experiment

- The .... of energy (from food) should .... the use of energy (for .... processes).

- The amount of energy in food is given in .... or kilojoules.

- We can measure the amount of .... in different foods by .... a food sample.

- The .... in the food is used to raise the temperature of the .... in a test tube.

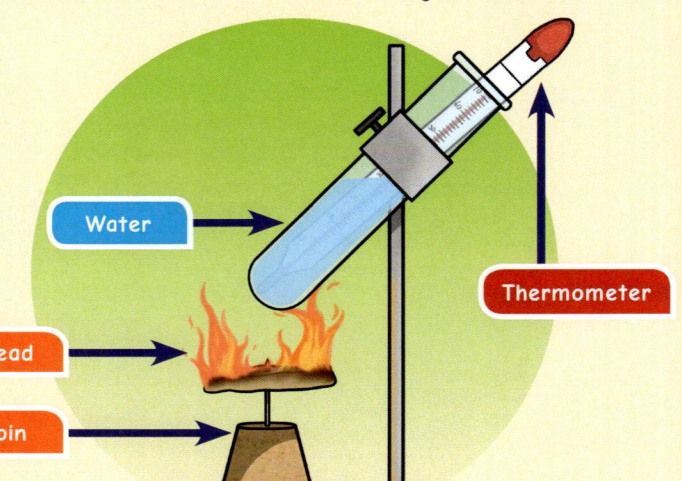

Water

Thermometer

Burning bread

Cork and pin

21   Dependent Variable

- .... the temperature of the water before you start each test.

- Measure the water temperature at the .... of each test.

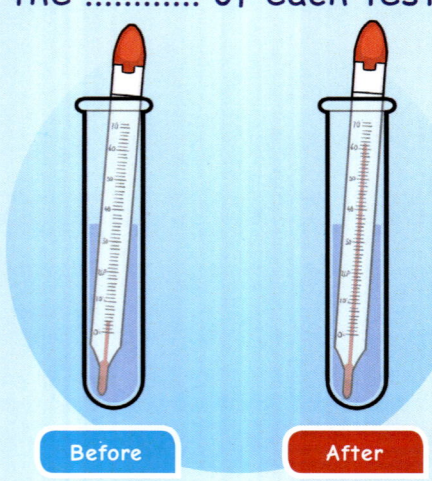

Before

After

22   Independent Variables

- Make sure you use the same .... (g) of each food type.

- Make sure you use the same amount of water for each test.

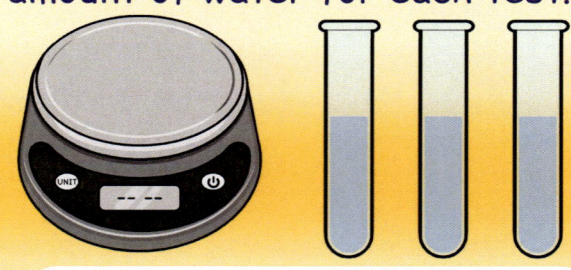

Always use the .... amount!

- It takes 4.2J to make the temperature of 1cm^3 of water rise by 1°C.

23 — Sankey Diagram: Bicycle

• We can use .... diagrams to show the .... transfers.

• When we ...., the 'energy in' is chemical energy from the .... we eat.

• The 'useful energy ......' is kinetic energy (........................... energy) making the .... go round.

• The .... energy is thermal energy.

Chemical Energy in

Wasted Energy: Thermal

Useful Kinetic Energy out

24 — Sankey Diagram: Filament ....

• If we measure the .... energy out and the .... energy in we can work out the percentage efficiency.

• The .... the percentage efficiency, the .... energy is wasted.

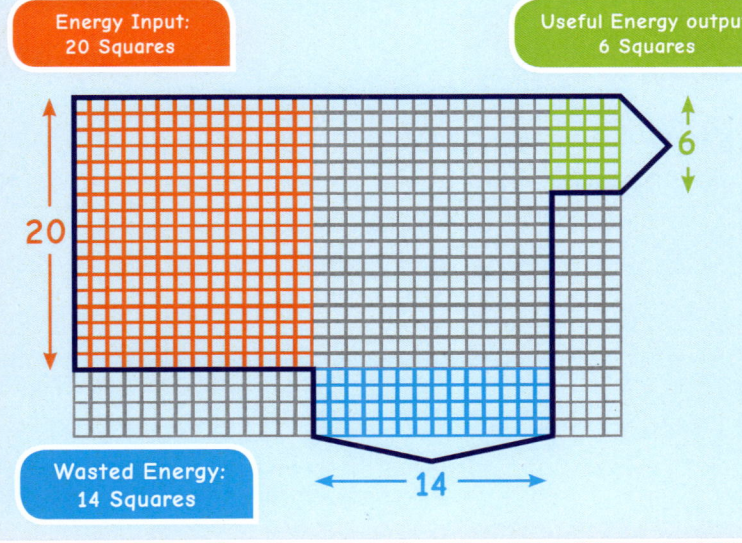

Energy Input: 20 Squares

Useful Energy output: 6 Squares

20

6

14

Wasted Energy: 14 Squares

How to find the percentage efficiency:

% efficiency = $\dfrac{\text{Useful energy out}}{\text{...........................}}$ X100

$\dfrac{6 \text{ Squares}}{20 \text{ Squares}}$ X100 = 30% efficiency

25   Useful and Wasted Energy

- Let's look at the useful and wasted energy in each of these devices.

Torch		Bell		Laptop	
Useful	Wasted	Useful	Wasted	Useful	Wasted
.... Energy	.... Energy	.... Energy	.... Energy	Sound Energy / Light Energy	.... Energy

26   Sankey Diagram: Torch

- The useful energy from a torch is light energy.

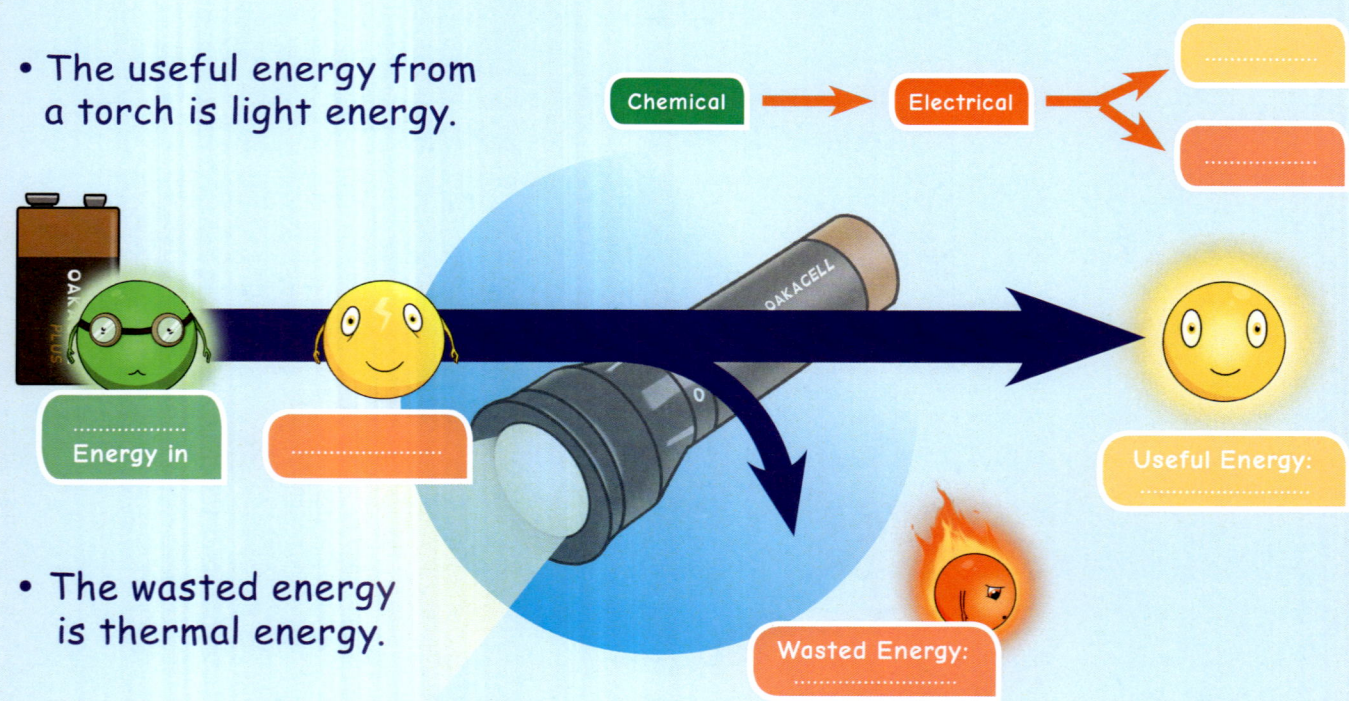

Chemical → Electrical → .... / ....

Energy in   ....

Useful Energy: ....

Wasted Energy: ....

- The wasted energy is thermal energy.

27 Sankey Diagram: Bell

- The useful energy from the bell is sound energy.

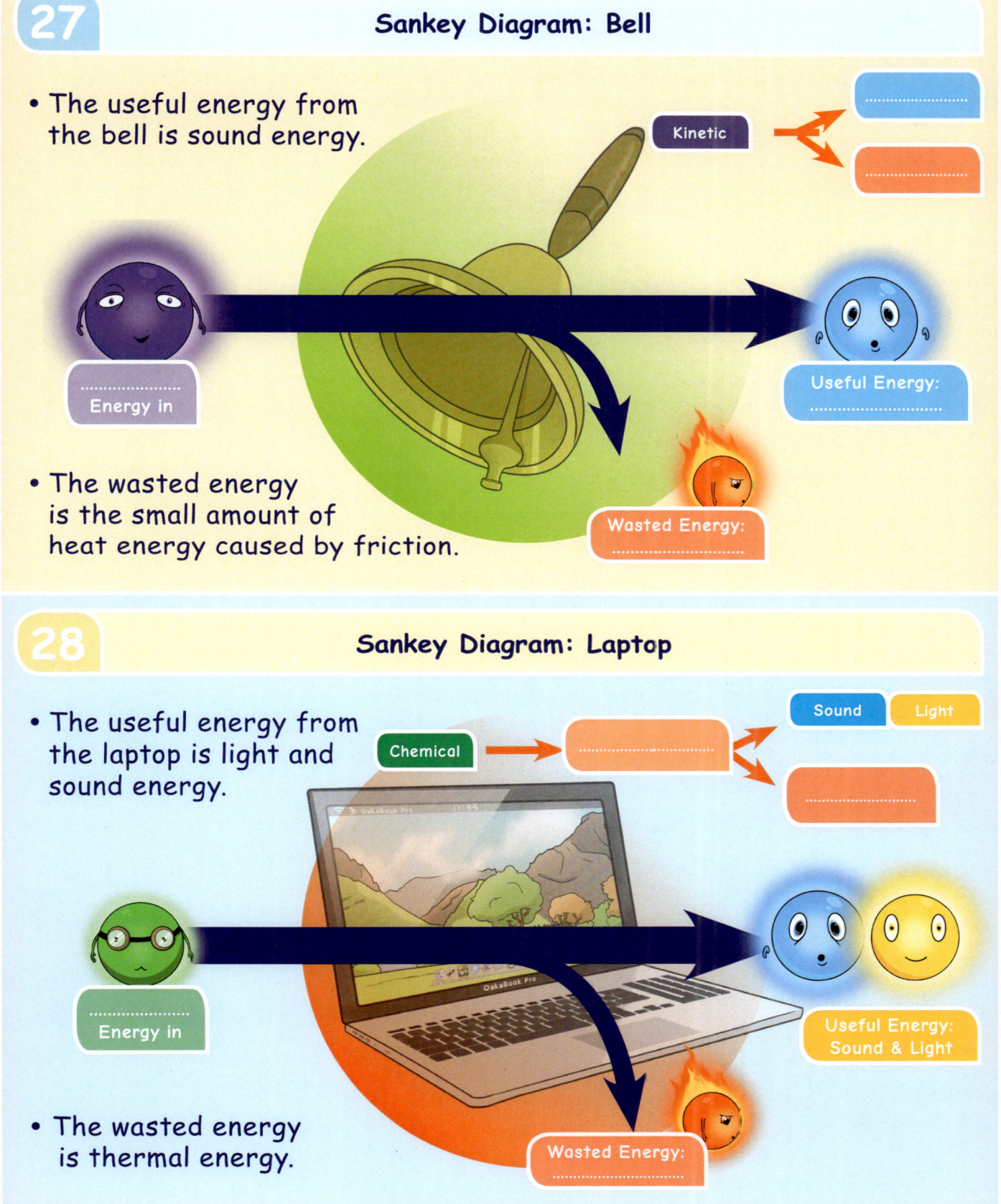

Kinetic

Energy in

Useful Energy:
....

Wasted Energy:
....

- The wasted energy is the small amount of heat energy caused by friction.

28 Sankey Diagram: Laptop

- The useful energy from the laptop is light and sound energy.

Chemical

Sound   Light

....

....

Energy in

Useful Energy:
Sound & Light

Wasted Energy:
....

- The wasted energy is thermal energy.

29   Energy Saving Bulbs

- We can save .... by using more .... devices.

- Energy .... lamps are much more efficient than .... lamps.

- Energy saving lamps use much less ....

- They waste much less electricity than ....

- .... lamps are the most efficient.

Filament Lightbulb

40W
Life Expectancy:
1 Year

Energy Saving Lightbulb

11W
Life Expectancy:
6 - 10 Years

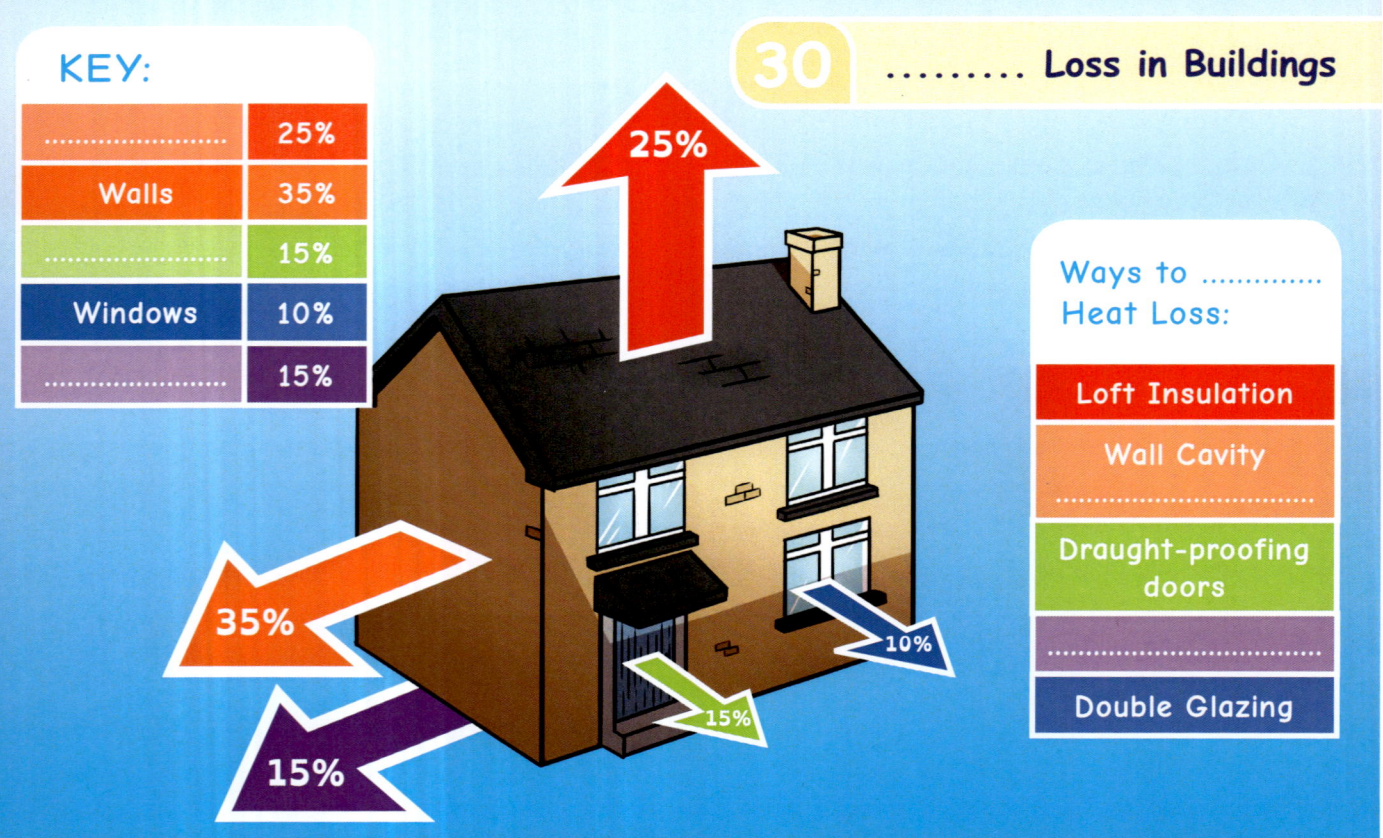

KEY:

....	25%
Walls	35%
....	15%
Windows	10%
....	15%

30   .... Loss in Buildings

25%

35%

10%

15%

Ways to .... Heat Loss:

Loft Insulation
Wall Cavity ....
Draught-proofing doors
....
Double Glazing

31 .... Emission Energy

- Power stations transfer ...., nuclear, ..., heat and kinetic energy into .... energy.

Chemical   Nuclear   Solar

Thermal   Kinetic

Electrical

- .... fuel power stations cause a lot of ....

32 Low .... Energy

- Wind, wave and hydroelectric power stations .... very .... pollution.

....

....

....

How Power Stations Work

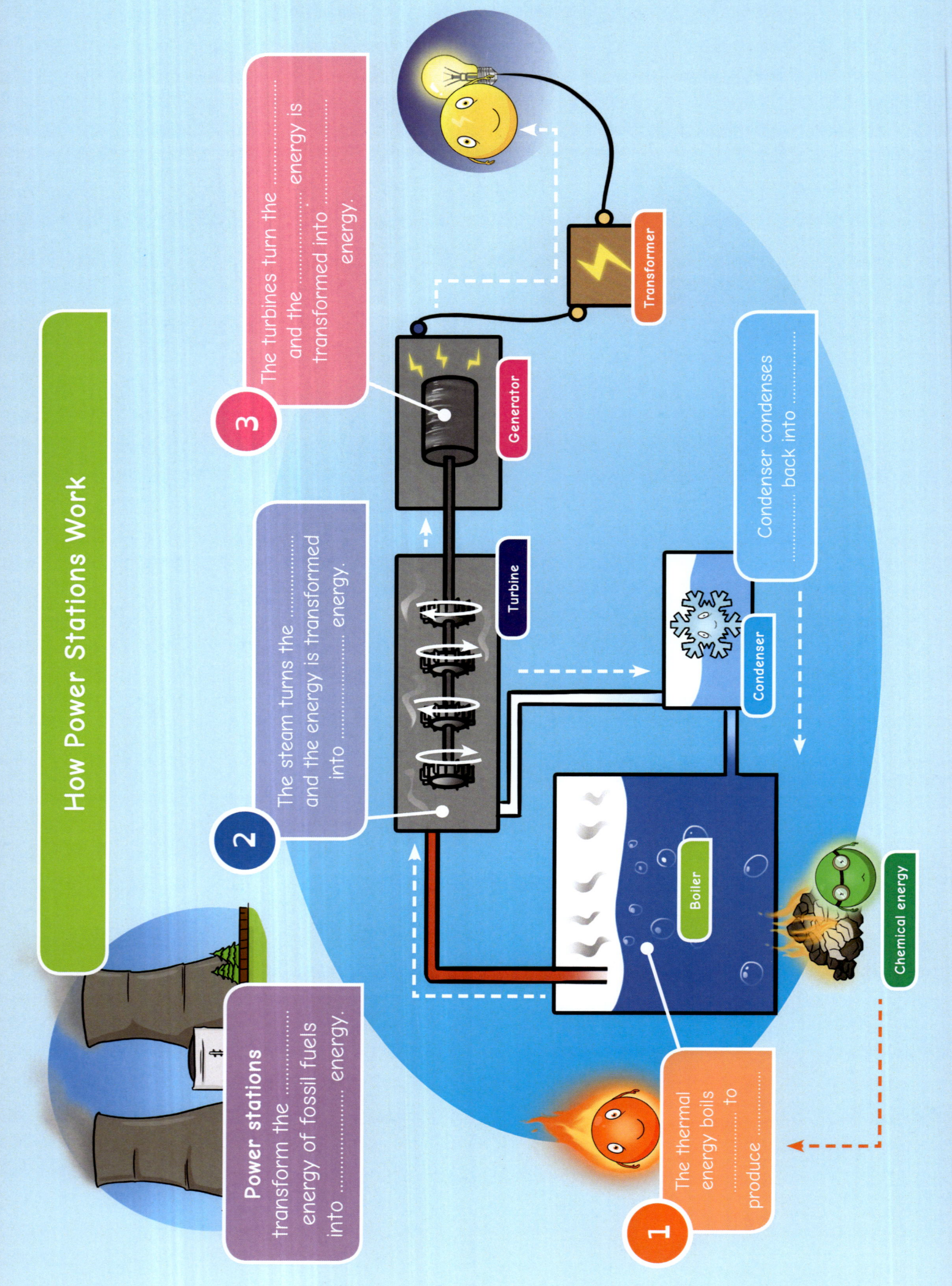

Power stations transform the .... energy of fossil fuels into .... energy.

1 The thermal energy boils .... to produce ....

Chemical energy

Boiler

Condenser condenses .... back into ....

Condenser

2 The steam turns the .... and the energy is transformed into .... energy.

Turbine

3 The turbines turn the .... and the .... energy is transformed into .... energy.

Generator

Transformer

The Useful Energy in the Sun

Animals ....

They die and get ....

Become ....
and ....

Buried to form ....

.... power

Light for plants to grow

Plants die

.... fuel

Rain is trapped behind ....

Heat evaporates water from oceans and lakes

Evaporated water rises

It condenses and falls as ....

Air heated more in some places than others

hot air rises

cold air falls

Wind makes ....

Causes ....

Waves turn ....

Wind turns turbines

33 Power is Measured in Watts (W)

• .... tells us how much energy we are using each ....

• Power is measured in .... (W).

Power is measured in watts (W)

34 Workout the power!

The current = 5A

The voltage = 12V

• To work out the **power** in a simple circuit:

power = ... × current

SO....

12V X 5A = ...

The power is ....!

35 What Are Joules?

• We measure .... in joules.

• 1 Watt = 1 Joule of electrical energy .... per second.

• These are very .... units!

36 How To .... Energy

• To work out how much we pay for .... we use kilowatt hours (............).

1 kW = 1000 watts

X

1 hour = 3,600 seconds

• If 1,000 Watts are in a kilowatt and 3,600 seconds are in 1 hour. We times these together and this gives us 1 kWh.

=

1 kWh = 3,600,000 j